Specimen Sight-Reading Tests for Treble Recorder

Grades 6-8

The Associated Board of
the Royal Schools of Music

GRADE 6

1

2

© 1996 by The Associated Board of the Royal Schools of Music

AB 2517

3

Allegretto espressivo

4

Con moto

5

Allegro giocoso

6

Allegro

9 **Molto andante**

10 **Moderato**

GRADE 7

Moderato – leggiero e delicato

Andante espressivo

GRADE 8

1

2

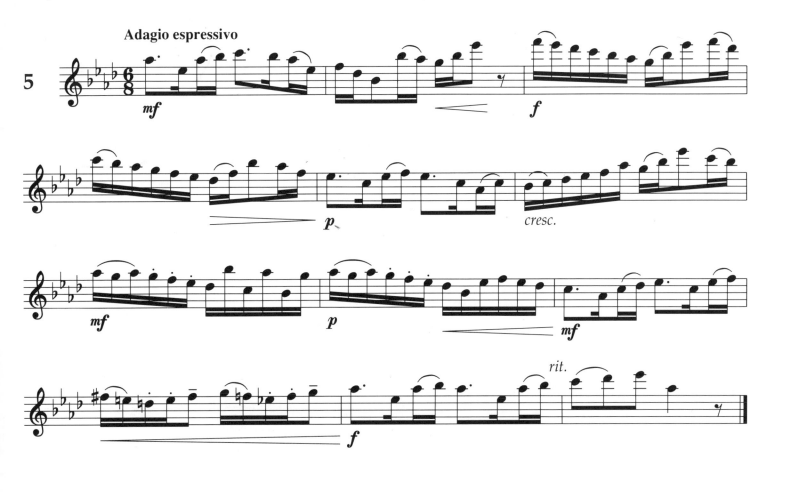

Allegretto grazioso e delicato

7

Moderato tranquillo

8

11

12

Typeset by Musonix